Collins · *do brilliantly!*

PracticePapers

KS3 Science

Ray Oliver

Published by HarperCollins*Publishers* Ltd
77–85 Fulham Palace Road
London W6 8JB

www.collinseducation.com

© HarperCollins*Publishers* Ltd 2004

First published 2004

10 9 8 7 6 5 4 3
ISBN-13 978 0 00 717803 2
ISBN-10 0 00 717803 4

Ray Oliver asserts the moral right to be identified as the author of this work.

British Library Cataloguing in Publication Data
A catalogue record for this book is available from the British Library.

Production by Katie Butler
Design by Chi Leung
Printed and bound by Printing Express, Hong Kong

Illustrations
Pat Murray

www.fireandwater.com
Visit the book lover's website

Contents

What are the National Tests?

The education of children in the UK is divided into sections that are known as key stages. At infant and primary schools, children are at Key Stages 1 and 2. Secondary education begins with Key Stage 3 (KS3) and this covers the first three years of secondary schooling. We call these years 7, 8 and 9. In year 10 students move on to the next key stage, Key Stage 4. This is when students spend two years preparing for their GCSE examinations, which are completed in year 11.

There are National Tests for all students that are organised by a government body known as the Qualifications and Curriculum Authority (QCA). These tests are designed to measure the progress students have made as they reach the end of a key stage. In the case of secondary schools, these KS3 tests (called the SATs) are taken in May of year 9. The test papers are marked externally, rather like GCSE examinations. The results are reported to schools and students before the end of the summer term, usually in early July.

Although schools are required to report their students' progress in all subjects, only three subjects are assessed by formal national tests. These subjects are:
- English;
- Mathematics;
- Science.

The National Tests in these subjects are not the only way in which the progress of each student is assessed.

Teacher Assessment

Teacher assessment is regarded as an essential part of the National Curriculum assessment and reporting arrangements, according to the QCA. Teachers must keep records of every student and update them regularly. All subjects, not just English, Mathematics and Science, include teacher assessment.

Attainment Targets

School subjects are divided into separate sections of work known as attainment targets. Details of the Science attainment targets are given below.

In each attainment target, or section of study, students may be working at different levels, according to their abilities. The levels each have a reference number. For example, a child may achieve level 4 in English at the end of primary schooling (the end of KS2). By the end of the key stage tests in year 9, this child may have progressed to level 5, 6 or 7 within the same area of study. Most school subjects are divided into several attainment targets (ATs). For example:

Subject	number of ATs (= sections)
English	3
Mathematics	4
Science	4
History	1

The overall subject level achieved by a student will be calculated from the separate levels for each of the attainment targets. For example, in English, a child achieving levels 4, 5 and 6 in the three attainment targets, will be awarded the average, level 5. In Mathematics the situation is more complicated since the attainment targets do not carry equal weighting; some are regarded as more important. In the case of Mathematics, the overall subject level is not a simple average score.

Science National Tests at KS3 (the year 9 SATs)

The National Curriculum in Science is divided into four sections or four attainment targets:

* Sc1   Scientific Enquiry
This covers experimental work and laboratory investigations. An example would be as follows:
What are the factors that affect how fast a chemical reaction can go?

* Sc2   Life Processes and Living Things
This is the biology section and covers such topics as:
Cells and cell functions
Humans as organisms
The environment

*Sc3   Materials and their Properties
This is the Chemistry and Earth Sciences (Geology) section. It covers such topics as:
Classification of materials
Patterns of chemical behaviour
Geological changes

*Sc4   Physical Changes
This is the Physics section and covers such topics as:
Electricity and magnetism
Forces and motion
The earth and beyond

Each of the four attainment targets in science (Sc1 to Sc4) is given equal importance.

This is how they are assessed:

Attainment target	Assessment method
Sc1	National Test in year 9
Sc2	National Test in year 9
Sc3	National Test in year 9
Sc4	National Test in year 9

The year 9 Science tests are available in two different ranges of levels, known as tiers. The less demanding papers are Tiers 3–6 covering levels 3 to 6 of the National Curriculum. The more difficult papers are Tiers 5–7 covering levels 5 to 7 of the National Curriculum.

Students are entered by their school for the tier that matches their recent performance in Science. Each paper contains questions from all of the Science attainment targets (Enquiry, Biology, Chemistry and Physics). Students have to take both Paper 1 and Paper 2 of the same tier, say the 3–6 tier.

How can I prepare for the National Tests?

This book has been designed to give you the best possible chance of success in the year 9 National Tests. The way to find out if you really understand a topic is simple – try to answer questions on that topic.

This book has been written in order to:

- cover all of the main topics you are likely to meet in the exam;
- give you questions that are very similar in style to the year 9 tests;
- give you detailed answers and advice about how to achieve top marks;
- give you a choice of levels to try, just like the real exams:
  Paper 1 levels 3–6 or levels 5–7;
  Paper 2 levels 3–6 or 5–7;
- encourage you to improve your performance by trying the test papers more than once.

How should I use this book?

The way to get the most from this book is very simple. Follow these steps:

- **Step 1** Choose a topic, for example, magnetism or fuels;
- **Step 2** Spend 15 minutes revising the topic first. Revision could use:
  * your class notes;
  * your textbook;
  * the web.
- **Step 3** Scan through the questions in this book until you find one on the same topic
- **Step 4** Try the question
- **Step 5** Look at the mark scheme for the question. Were there any problems? Read the answers and the advice given. Next time you will be able to gain full marks on a question like this.

Revision may seem very, very boring. The trick is to use your time effectively so that it does not take up all your free time. Successful revision means a little and often.

Taking the full test and finding your national level

When the real year 9 National Test is getting near, try a complete Paper 1 and Paper 2. Choose either the 3–6 level papers or the 5–7 level papers. You could even try both. If you do both, you will notice that some of the questions are the same in both papers. This follows the style of the National Test papers and for revision purposes will help you gauge the level at which you are working.

- Write your answers;
- Use the mark scheme to find your total score;
- Add your scores for Papers 1 and 2;
- Check the mark scheme table to see the level you have achieved.

For example, if you scored a total of 128 marks on the level 3–6 papers, you are working at level 5, about the national average level. But look carefully at the table. You need only another 6 marks to move up to level 6. Be ambitious.

Paper 1

Tier 3–6

- The test is 1 hour long.

- You will need: pen, pencil, rubber, ruler, protractor and calculator.

- The test starts with easier questions.

- Write all your answers on the test paper – do not use any rough paper.

- Check your work carefully.

- Ask your teacher if you are not sure what to do.

1. The drawing shows heavy horses being used on a farm to plough a field.

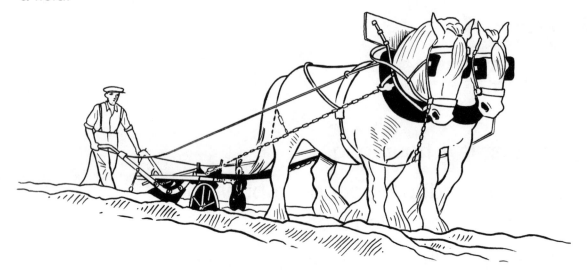

Some farmers prefer horses to tractors since they cause less damage to the soil. Pulling a plough is hard work. It can take many hours to plough one large field.

(a) Which two features would a farmer prefer when selecting new work horses?
Choose from this list and give reasons.

lively nature   strong legs   full mane
brown eyes   thick coat   calm nature

First choice _____   *1 mark*

reason _____   *1 mark*

Second choice _____   *1 mark*

reason _____   *1 mark*

(b) Horse breeders find that when a foal (baby horse) is born, it resembles its parents. Why does a foal resemble its father? Underline the correct word.

Genetic information is carried in: an egg / sperm / blood.   *1 mark*

(c) Horse breeders say that foals from the same parents show variation. What does this mean?

_____   *1 mark*

Total Score [ ]

maximum 6 marks

8

2. Careful observation of a garden bird showed that it ate the following numbers of other creatures.

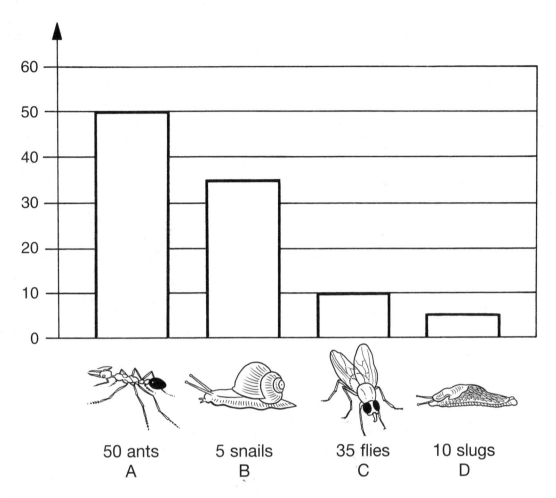

50 ants   5 snails   35 flies   10 slugs
A   B   C   D

(a) Write the correct letter (A-D) in each bar of the bar chart.   *3 marks*

(b) A hedgehog moved in to the garden and was observed to eat slugs. How might this affect the garden bird?

_____

_____   *2 marks*

(c) The gardener sprayed the garden with a fly and ant killer. Describe one effect this might have on other wildlife in the garden.

_____

_____   *2 marks*

Total Score ☐

maximum 7 marks

9

3. A group of students investigated the best conditions for seeds to grow. This is what they did.

1	2	3	4
seeds + damp cotton wool	same as 1 but kept in fridge	same as 1 but kept at 100°C	seeds + dry cotton wool

(a) Seeds started to grow in tube 1. Name two things that these seeds probably needed to start growing.

_____   *2 marks*

(b) What variable was being investigated in tubes 2 and 3?

_____   *1 mark*

(c) No seeds grew in tube 4. Suggest a reason for this.

_____   *1 mark*

(d) One student suggested covering a tube in aluminium kitchen foil. What variable would this allow the students to investigate?

_____   *1 mark*

Total Score	

maximum 5 marks

4. Mixtures can be separated in different ways. Look at this drawing of a mixture being separated.

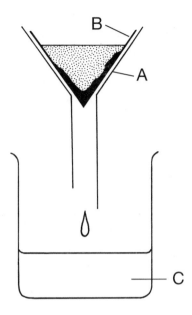

(a) Name the parts of the filtration apparatus.

A is _____

B is _____

C is _____   2 marks

(b) (i) Which of the following mixtures can be separated by filtration? Tick any correct answers.

Food dyes in water   ☐

Sawdust in water   ☐

Orange juice in water   ☐   1 mark

(ii) If you filtered a mixture of sand and sea water, where would the sand be at the end?

_____   1 mark

(c) Which method of separation could be used to obtain drinking water from seawater?

_____   1 mark

Total Score ☐

maximum 5 marks

11

5. Sara was asked to separate pieces of metal from other waste material so that it could be recycled. The table shows the properties of the materials.

Material	Shiny	Conducts electricity	Insulator
P	Yes	No	Yes
Q	Yes	Yes	No
R	No	No	yes

(a)   Which material was probably a metal? Give a reason.

_____

_____   *2 marks*

(b)   Which other properties in the following list are found in **all** common metals? Underline any correct answers.

   silvery   brittle   bends without breaking   conducts heat   *1 mark*

(c)   Sara wanted to check whether drinks cans were made of steel or aluminium. How should she test them?

_____   *1 mark*

(d)   Sara found that a copper coin went black when heated strongly in a Bunsen flame. Explain why the colour changed.

_____

_____   *2 marks*

Total Score

maximum 6 marks

6. Some students investigated the effect of burning different fuels on the temperature of water. In each case, 1g of the fuel was burned underneath a beaker containing 100 ml water at 20°C. Here are the results.

Fuel	Temperature at start (°C)	Temperature at end (°C)	Observations
Ethanol (alcohol)	20	34	Clear blue flame
Candle	20	28	Yellow flame, some soot
Paraffin	20	36	Yellow flame, smoke and soot

(a) (i) Which fuel released most heat?

_____   *1 mark*

(ii) All three fuels release a gas that can turn lime water cloudy. Name this gas.

_____   *1 mark*

(b) Using the information in the table, which fuel burns most cleanly?

_____   *1 mark*

(c) Ethanol is described as a renewable fuel. What does this mean?

_____

_____   *2 marks*

Total Score [   ]

maximum 5 marks

13

7. Sometimes the Earth comes in between the Sun and the Moon.

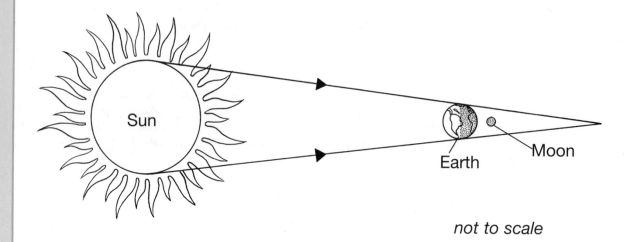

not to scale

(a) This is called a lunar eclipse. During a lunar eclipse, a curved shadow can be observed on the surface of the Moon, as seen from the Earth. Which two of these statements are correct? Tick the correct answers.

Light travels in a curved path. ☐

The curved Earth gives a curved shadow. ☐

Sunlight travels in straight lines. ☐

The Moon gives off its own light. ☐ *2 marks*

(b) Use the diagram above to explain why a lunar eclipse lasts for only a short time.

_____

_____ *2 marks*

(c) If a space traveller was on the Moon, what would the Sun look like during a lunar eclipse?

_____ *1 mark*

Total Score ☐
maximum 5 marks

8. Sam was investigating the way that sound travels through solids. First, he looked at this table in a data book.

Material	Speed of sound in metres/second
Air	330
Aluminium	5000
Clay tile	3500

(a) Through which material does sound travel fastest?

_____ *1 mark*

(b) (i) If Sam wanted to measure the speed of sound in air across a field, which of the following would **not** be needed? Tick the answer.

Distance the sound travelled in air _____

Time the sound took to travel _____

Speed of light in air _____ *1 mark*

(ii) Here are Sam's results for the speed of sound in air.

Experiment	Speed of sound in metres/second
A	280
B	410
C	300

Should Sam repeat any of these experiments? Explain your answer.

_____

_____ *2 marks*

Total Score [ ]

maximum 4 marks

15

9. When a large gun is fired, there is a flash of light and a loud noise.

   (a) An observer who was one kilometre away from the gun saw the flash as it was fired. She did not hear the noise for a few seconds. Explain the reason.

   _____

   _____ *2 marks*

   (b) (i) A series of observers at different distances from the gun recorded what they saw and heard.

Observer	Time between seeing gun fire and hearing the noise, in seconds
A	3.0
B	7.0
C	1.5
D	8.5
E	4.0
F	14.0
G	6.5

   Which observer was closest to the gun?

   _____ *1 mark*

   (ii) An extra observer H was half way between observers B and F. How long did the noise take to reach observer H? Explain your answer.

   _____

   _____ *2 marks*

Total Score

maximum 5 marks

16

10. The drawing shows a tent used by a group of naturalists on a small island.

(a) They needed electricity to run the fridge and to cook food.
Draw a line below to join each of these to its source of energy.

Source of energy

sunlight

to cook food   plants

to run the fridge   flowing water

heat from the Sun   *2 marks*

(b) (i) In the dry season, little water flows in the stream. How would this affect the group?

_____   *1 mark*

(ii) Using the drawing, suggest one alternative source of fuel they could use for cooking.

_____   *1 mark*

Total Score [ ]

maximum 4 marks

11. The drawing shows the human skeleton.

skull

B

rib cage

A

elbow

radius and
ulna

pelvis

C

knee

vertebrae

back bone

(a) Some parts of the skeleton protect vital organs. Which part protects the heart and lungs?

_____   *1 mark*

(b) From the drawing, write the letter that labels:

(i) the humerus _____   *1 mark*

(ii) the femur _____   *1 mark*

(iii) the collar bone _____   *1 mark*

(c) Describe how the shape of the knee bones allows the leg to bend.

_____

_____   *1 mark*

(d) The knee contains cartilage. How does this help movement?

_____

_____   *1 mark*

Total Score	

maximum 6 marks

12. The drawing shows part of the respiratory system.

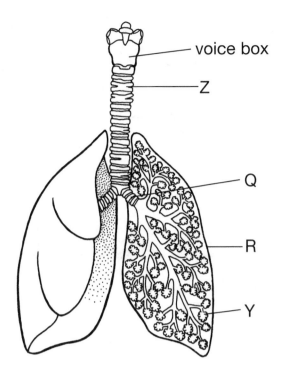

voice box

Z

Q

R

Y

(a) From the drawing, write the letter that labels:

(i) the windpipe _____   *1 mark*

(ii) alveoli _____   *1 mark*

(b) (i) Where does gas exchange happen?

_____   *1 mark*

(ii) Cigarette smoke contains carbon monoxide which can enter the blood. Why is this a problem?

_____   *1 mark*

(c) Oxygen and carbon monoxide compete to join with red blood cells. The muscles obtain the oxygen they need from red blood cells. Why are top athletes unlikely to be smokers?

_____

_____   *2 marks*

Total Score [ ]

maximum 6 marks

13. The diagram shows a section through the human female reproductive system, showing changes over 28 days.

lining breaks down   lining is building up   uterus lining fully thickened

Day 1   Day 10   Day 14   Day 17   Day 28

| Menstrual cycle starts | Lining starts to thicken | Egg released from ovary | Egg is travelling to uterus | If fertilised, the egg will stay in the uterus. If not, the lining breaks down. |

(a) (i) On which day is the egg released by the ovary?

_____ *1 mark*

(ii) Where does the egg travel to?

_____ *1 mark*

(b) Complete the sentences below by filling in the two gaps.

The breakdown of the lining of the uterus is known as

_____ .

The complete 28 day series of changes is known as the

_____ . *2 marks*

(c) After fertilisation, the egg passes into the uterus and attaches itself to the lining.
(i) Why is the lining full of blood vessels?

_____

_____ *1 mark*

(ii) After about nine months the baby is born. How does the uterus help?

_____

_____ *1 mark*

Total Score

maximum 6 marks

14. Chris wanted to investigate physical and chemical changes. He put three different chemicals into separate test tubes. Each tube had a loose plug of mineral wool at the top. He weighed the tubes before and after heating, waiting until each tube was cold.

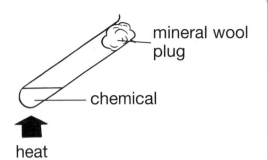

mineral wool plug

chemical

heat

He recorded his observations in a table:

Experiment	Name of chemical	Observations	Change in mass
X	Calcium, a silver-coloured solid	Burned brightly with an orange flame, leaving a white solid	Increased
Y	Silicon dioxide, a yellow powder	Powder stayed as separate grains, still same colour at end	No change
Z	Potassium nitrate, white crystals	Solid melted then bubbled, went solid again on cooling	Decrease

(a) (i) In experiment X, the calcium reacted with one of the gases in the air.
Complete the word equation for the reaction of calcium in experiment X.

Calcium + _____ → _____   *2 marks*

(ii) Explain why the mass changed in experiment X.

_____

_____   *1 mark*

(b) What was the reason for using the mineral wool plug?

_____

_____   *1 mark*

(c) Name the yellow chemical left at the end in experiment Y.

_____   *1 mark*

(d) In each experiment, did a physical or a chemical change take place? Tick one box for each experiment.

experiment	chemical change	physical change
X	☐	☐
Y	☐	☐
Z	☐	☐

1 mark

Total Score ☐

maximum 6 marks

15. (a) The element bromine can be a solid, a liquid or a gas. Each change of state has its own name.

(i) The process of changing from solid to liquid is called

_____ . *1 mark*

(ii) Liquid bromine is brown. At room temperature, a brown gas can be seen above the surface of liquid bromine. Explain why.

_____

_____ *2 marks*

(iii) Draw the arrangement of particles in bromine gas inside the box.

```
┌─────────────────────┐
│                     │
│                     │
│                     │
└─────────────────────┘
```

2 marks

(b) The boiling point of bromine is 59°C and its melting point is -7° Celsius.

(i) What is the physical state of bromine at 0°C?

_____ *1 mark*

(ii) Are the particles of bromine closer together at 0°C or at 60°C?

_____

_____ *2 marks*

Total Score [ ]

maximum 8 marks

16. Jo wanted to use four lamps to light a mirror on a dressing table. She worked out two ways to connect the lamps.

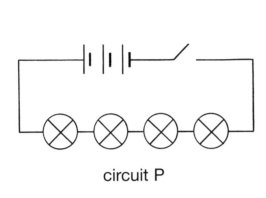

circuit P

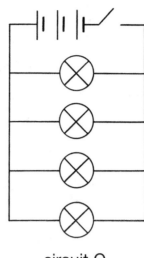

circuit Q

(a) (i) One of the lamps was broken. Which circuit still worked with the other lamps shining? Explain why.

_____

_____ *2 marks*

(ii) What type of circuit is the one that did not work with the broken lamp?

_____ *1 mark*

(b) (i) Jo noticed that the lamps were hot to touch when they were switched on. Fill in the gaps to show the energy changes in the lamps.

Electrical energy $\longrightarrow$ _____ + _____ *2 marks*

(ii) What type of energy is being wasted?

_____ *1 mark*

Total Score ☐

maximum 6 marks

23

17. Al was investigating contact forces at the swimming pool.

slide

swimming pool

A friend timed how long each turn on the slide took. The results are shown in the table.

Experiment number	Conditions	Time in seconds
1	Dry slide and dry costume	8
2	Dry slide and wet costume	7
3	Water poured first on the slide	5

(a) What is the name of the contact force between the slide and the person sliding down?

_____ *1 mark*

(b) (i) What pattern do you notice in the results?

_____

_____ *2 marks*

(ii) What part is played by the water in this experiment?

_____ *1 mark*

Total Score

maximum 4 marks

Paper 2
Tier 3–6

- The test is 1 hour long.

- You will need: pen, pencil, rubber, ruler, protractor and calculator.

- The test starts with easier questions.

- Write all your answers on the test paper – do not use any rough paper.

- Check your work carefully.

- Ask your teacher if you are not sure what to do.

1. Chris is holding a model parachute at the top of a hill.

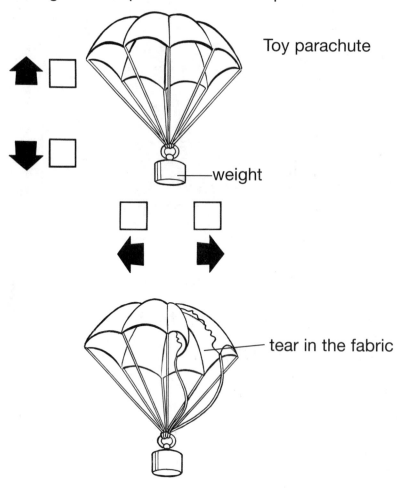

(a) Which arrow shows the direction of the force of gravity acting on the parachute? Tick the box next to the correct arrow. *1 mark*

(b) Chris lets go of the parachute. If there is no wind that day, in which direction will it start to move?

_____ *1 mark*

(c) After a short time Chris sees that the parachute is moving at a steady speed. What does this tell us about the forces acting on the parachute?

_____ *1 mark*

(d) When Chris tries the parachute again, he finds that there is a tear in the fabric. How will this affect the speed with which it moves? Explain your answer.

_____

_____ *2 marks*

Total Score [   ]

maximum 5 marks

26

2. The planets are held in orbit around the Sun by the Sun's gravitational pull. The strength of the pull depends on the distance between them and on the mass of the planet.

(a) The order of the inner planets starting from the Sun is:

Mercury   Venus   Earth   Mars

The Earth and Venus are of similar size. Which of these two planets experiences a greater pull? Explain your answer.

_____

_____   *2 marks*

(b) (i) Comets are also pulled by the Sun's gravity. Halley's Comet comes close to the Sun every 76 years as it moves round and round. How many times does the Earth go round the Sun in one orbit of Halley's Comet?

_____   *1 mark*

(ii) We cannot observe the planets all the time because the Earth rotates on its axis. How long does one rotation take?

_____   *1 mark*

Total Score [ ]

maximum 4 marks

3. Mark was thinking about the advantages and disadvantages of using fossil fuels.

Name of fossil fuel	State	Burning produces
Coal	Solid	Carbon dioxide + traces of sulphur dioxide
Oil	Liquid	Carbon dioxide + less sulphur dioxide
Natural gas	Gas	Carbon dioxide

(a) (i) What do we mean by a fossil fuel?

_____   *1 mark*

(ii) Which fossil fuel is the most difficult to transport to where it is needed? Explain your answer.

_____

_____   *2 marks*

(b) All fossil fuels when they burn release a material that may be causing global warming. Name the material.

_____   *1 mark*

(c) (i) Some fossil fuels on burning release a material that causes acid rain. Name this material.

_____   *1 mark*

(ii) Many people want to use solar energy as an alternative to fossil fuels. How would this affect global warming?

_____   *1 mark*

Total Score

maximum 6 marks

4. A TV advert claimed that 'New Clean' was the best ever nail polish remover liquid. A pupil decided to investigate the claim.

The first part of the investigation was to put equal sized blobs of red nail polish onto glass slides. Next 10 drops of remover were added to a piece of cotton wool and this was wiped over the dry nail polish.

(a) Why did the pupil use equal sized blobs of nail polish?

_____ *1 mark*

(b) Describe two changes you would expect to see when the cotton wool was wiped on the slide.

_____

_____ *1 mark*

(c) How would the results allow the pupil to find which nail polish remover was the best?

_____

_____ *2 marks*

Total Score [ ]

maximum 4 marks

5. Chris used a bar magnet to magnetise some sewing needles.
The needles were then pushed through corks and floated on water.

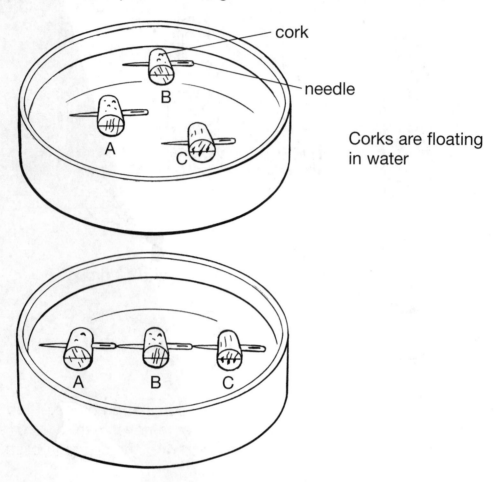

Corks are floating
in water

(a) When the corks were floating separately, they all pointed the same way. Explain why.

_____ *1 mark*

(b) When corks A, B and C were placed in a line, they stuck together. Explain why.

_____ *1 mark*

(c) When Chris brought the original bar magnet near cork A, the north pole of the bar magnet repelled the needlepoint. What kind of magnetic pole was the needlepoint?

_____ *1 mark*

(d) Chris decided to try the experiment again using copper needles but this time it didn't work. Why not?

_____ *1 mark*

Total Score	

maximum 4 marks

6. In the experiment below, chalk and acid react together to make carbon dioxide gas. This is the gas in fizzy drinks.

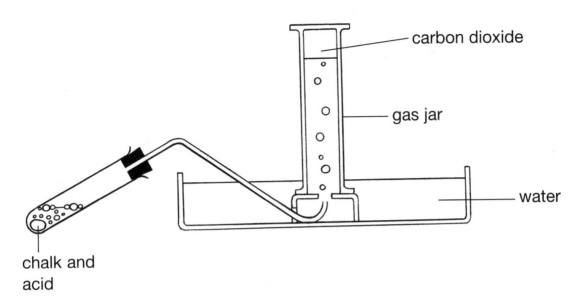

(a) What two pieces of evidence can you see to show that a gas is being produced?

_____

_____ *2 marks*

(b) (i) What can you tell from the experiment about the solubility of the gas in water?

_____ *1 mark*

(ii) When you open a bottle of fizzy drink, bubbles appear in the liquid. Explain why.

_____ *1 mark*

(c) Put the gases present in the air in order, starting with the one that makes up most of the air:

carbon dioxide   nitrogen   oxygen

_____ *1 mark*

Total Score ▢

maximum 5 marks

7. The diagram shows an extinct ('dead') volcano.

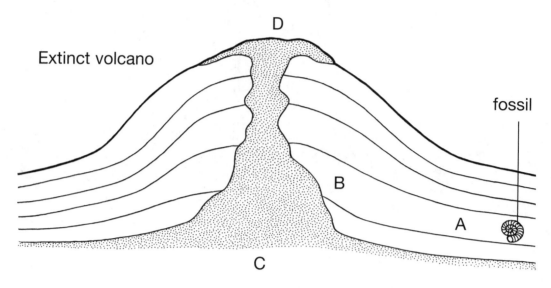

(a)   Rock A contains fossils. Name the type of rock that can contain fossils.

_____   *1 mark*

(b)   Rock B is in the same layer as A but it looks different and is much harder. What type of rock is this? Explain your answer.

_____

_____   *2 marks*

(c)   (i) Rock C contains a mass of crystals all quite large but in rock D the crystals are very small. Explain why there is a difference in terms of the active volcano.

_____

_____   *2 marks*

(ii) Rocks C and D are of the same type. What type is it?

_____   *1 mark*

(d)   Why don't we find fossils in rocks C and D?

_____   *1 mark*

Total Score [ ]

maximum 7 marks

8. Each of the animals below belongs to a different group.

(a) On the line beneath each drawing, write the name of the group to which the animal belongs. Choose from the list below:

mammals   arthropods   molluscs   insects   birds

A Slug

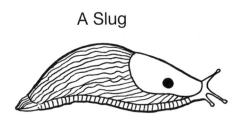

B Honey bee

_____   _____

C Dog   D Crab

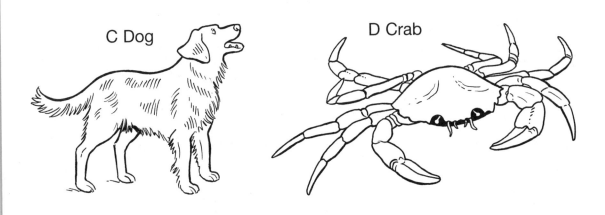

_____   _____

4 marks

(b) Which of the animals shown above is a vertebrate? Give the correct letter.

_____

1 mark

Total Score

maximum 5 marks

9. The list below gives the properties shown by different elements.

- high melting point
- low melting point
- good conductor of electricity
- poor conductor of electricity
- good conductor of heat
- poor conductor of heat
- shiny
- dense
- flexible, not brittle

(a) Which two properties of copper from the list above make it a good choice for house wiring?

_____

_____ *2 marks*

(b) Which property in the above list explains why:
(i) Mercury is a liquid metal

_____ *1 mark*

(ii) Aluminium is used for window frames

_____ *1 mark*

Total Score

maximum 4 marks

10. **(a)** Fran plays keyboard in a band.

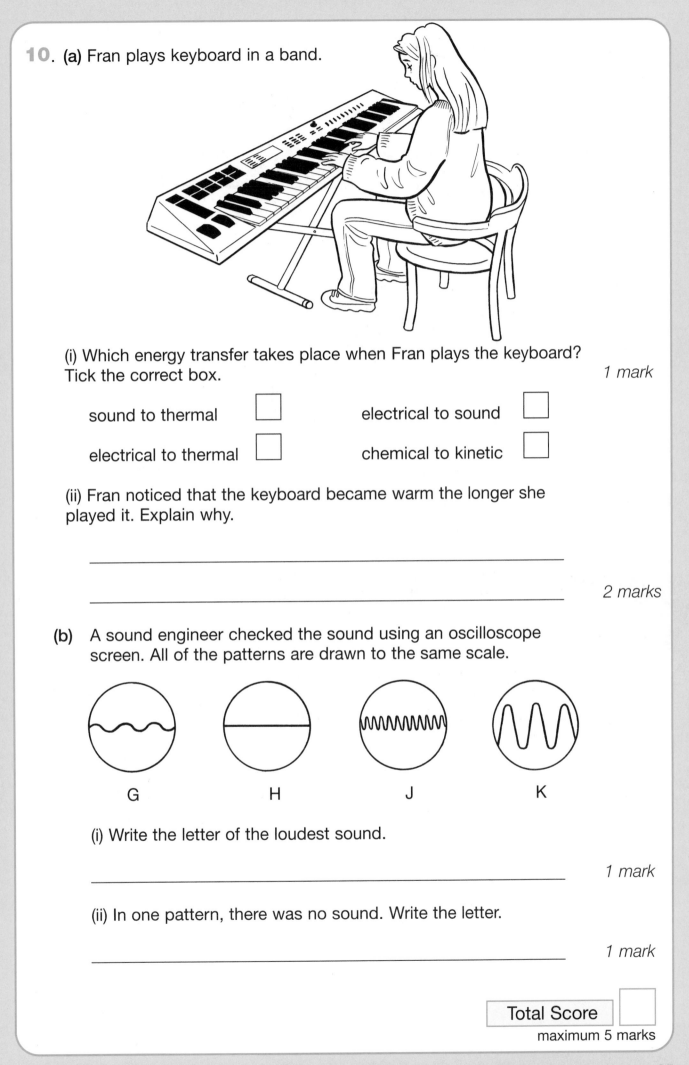

(i) Which energy transfer takes place when Fran plays the keyboard? Tick the correct box.

1 mark

sound to thermal ☐   electrical to sound ☐

electrical to thermal ☐   chemical to kinetic ☐

(ii) Fran noticed that the keyboard became warm the longer she played it. Explain why.

_____

_____

2 marks

(b) A sound engineer checked the sound using an oscilloscope screen. All of the patterns are drawn to the same scale.

    G   H   J   K

(i) Write the letter of the loudest sound.

_____

1 mark

(ii) In one pattern, there was no sound. Write the letter.

_____

1 mark

Total Score ☐

maximum 5 marks

11. Sunil is experimenting with a supermarket trolley.

(a) (i) Name the downward force acting on the trolley.

_____

1 mark

(ii) Draw arrows on the diagram showing the **two** horizontal
forces when Sunil is pushing the trolley along.

2 marks

(b) Sunil lets go of the trolley on a downward slope. Explain what
happens in terms of the forces acting on the trolley.

_____

_____

2 marks

(c) The trolley crashes into a wall and stops. Explain what has
happened to its kinetic energy.

_____

_____

2 marks

Total Score

maximum 7 marks

12. The science of burning caused arguments for many years. Here are some observations about burning materials in air. One scientist predicted that when materials burn, they always weigh less afterwards.

Experiment number	Material burned	Observations + mass changes
1	Candle	Wax melted, candle became smaller, mass decreased
2	Magnesium ribbon	Formed a solid white ash, mass increased
3	Charcoal	Glowed red, left a grey ash, mass decreased
4	Iron filings	Sparkled, left a grey solid, mass increased

(a) Does this evidence support the original prediction?
Explain your answer.

_____

_____ *2 marks*

(b) (i) In experiments 2 and 4 the product was a solid ash. In the other experiments, the products included gases. How could this help us understand the different mass changes?

_____

_____ *2 marks*

(ii) What further experiment needs to be done to see if the mass really falls or rises in experiment 1?

_____

_____ *1 mark*

Total Score

maximum 5 marks

13. Sara burned some hydrogen gas in a jet held just below a container of cold water.

(a) (i) Sara noticed that a liquid formed on the outside of the container. It was colourless and collected in the basin. Name this liquid.

_____ *1 mark*

(ii) The anhydrous (dried) copper sulphate turned from white to blue. Does this support your answer to part (i)?

_____

_____ *1 mark*

(b) (i) Explain why the flask was filled with cold water.

_____ *1 mark*

(ii) Containers of hydrogen have a hazard warning on them like this.

What does this sign mean?

_____ *1 mark*

(iii) Cylinders containing hydrogen gas should not be stored in direct sunlight. Explain why.

_____

_____ *2 marks*

Total Score

maximum 6 marks

14. Jack made saturated solutions of two chemicals at a range of temperatures. He found out how much solid had dissolved by weighing the tubes of solution each time. Here are the results. Solubility is measured in g of solid/kg water.

Chemical	0° Celsius	10	20	30	40	50	60	70
Potassium chloride	280		315	345	376	402	432	460	486
Sodium sulphate	45		92	210	412	482	464	450	438

(a) Jack decided to use the same size tube each time and the same volume of water. Explain why.

_____

_____ *2 marks*

(b) (i) What pattern do you see for the solution of potassium chloride?

_____ *1 mark*

(ii) How does sodium sulphate compare?

_____

_____ *1 mark*

Total Score

maximum 4 marks

15. The diagrams show cells from plants.

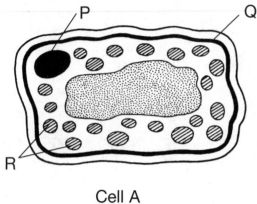

Cell A

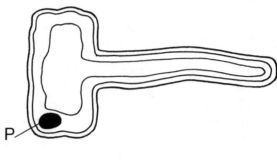

Cell B

(a) Letter P is the control centre for the cell.

We call it the _____ .   *1 mark*

(b) (i) What part of the cell is Q?

_____   *1 mark*

(ii) One of the cells takes part in photosynthesis. It is cell _____ .

The reason for this choice of answer is that _____ .

_____   *1 mark*

(c) (i) Complete the word equation for photosynthesis:

_____ _____ + water ———⟶ glucose + _____
                              light and a
                              green pigment   *2 marks*

(ii) Name the green pigment.

_____   *1 mark*

Total Score	
maximum 6 marks	

16. A balanced diet is essential to maintain good health. Part of this diet should be minerals and vitamins.

Mineral	Not enough of it	Foods that contain it
Calcium	Weak bones, teeth	Milk, green vegetables
Iron	Unhealthy blood cells (anaemia)	Meat, nuts
Sodium	Muscle cramps	Salt
Vitamin A	Poor eyesight, skin problems	Milk, butter, carrots
Vitamin C	Bleeding gums, loose teeth (scurvy)	Lemons, oranges, tomatoes.

(a) Name a source of iron in the diet.

_____ *1 mark*

(b) (i) Some people do not eat meat. How can they obtain the iron they need?

_____ *1 mark*

(ii) Two hundred years ago, before the invention of fridges or tinned food, sailors could not obtain enough fresh fruit or vegetables on long voyages. What health problems might this cause?

_____

_____ *2 marks*

(c) Which mineral is needed for strong bones?

_____ *1 mark*

Total Score

maximum 5 marks

17. Colours can look different in daylight and in artificial light.

The colours of the spotlight keep changing. One dancer's sweatshirt looks like this:

Spotlight colour	Sweatshirt looked
red	red
blue	blue
green	green

(a) What colour is the sweatshirt in daylight? Explain your answer.

_____

_____ *2 marks*

(b) (i) Another dancer's shirt looked green in daylight but black in a blue spotlight. Explain why.

_____

_____ *2 marks*

(ii) In clothes shops some customers ask to take the clothes near a window or door before buying them. Explain why.

_____ *1 mark*

Total Score ☐

maximum 5 marks

Paper 1
Tier 5–7

- The test is 1 hour long.

- You will need: pen, pencil, rubber, ruler, protractor and calculator.

- The test starts with easier questions.

- Write all your answers on the test paper – do not use any rough paper.

- Check your work carefully.

- Ask your teacher if you are not sure what to do.

1. The drawing shows the human skeleton.

skull

B

rib cage

A

elbow

radius and ulna

vertebrae — back bone

C

pelvis

knee

(a)   Some parts of the skeleton protect vital organs. Which part protects the heart and lungs?

_____   *1 mark*

(b)   From the drawing, write the letter that labels:

(i) the humerus _____   *1 mark*

(ii) the femur _____   *1 mark*

(iii) the collar bone _____   *1 mark*

(c)   Describe how the shape of the knee bones allows the leg to bend.

_____

_____   *1 mark*

(d)   The knee contains cartilage. How does this help movement?

_____

_____   *1 mark*

| Total Score | |
maximum 6 marks

2. The drawing shows part of the respiratory system.

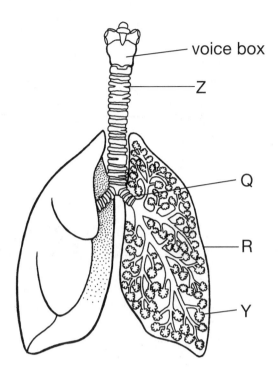

voice box

Z

Q

R

Y

(a) From the drawing, write the letter that labels:

(i) the windpipe _____   *1 mark*

(ii) alveoli _____   *1 mark*

(b) (i) Where does gas exchange happen?

_____   *1 mark*

(ii) Cigarette smoke contains carbon monoxide which can enter the blood. Why is this a problem?

_____   *1 mark*

(c) Oxygen and carbon monoxide compete to join with red blood cells. The muscles obtain the oxygen they need from red blood cells. Why are top athletes unlikely to be smokers?

_____

_____   *2 marks*

Total Score

maximum 6 marks

3. The diagram shows a section through the human female reproductive system, showing changes over 28 days.

lining breaks down   lining is building up   uterus lining fully thickened

Day 1   Day 10   Day 14 Day 17   Day 28

| Menstrual cycle starts | Lining starts to thicken | Egg released from ovary | Egg is travelling to uterus | If fertilised, the egg will stay in the uterus. If not, the lining breaks down. |

(a) (i) On which day is the egg released by the ovary?

_____ *1 mark*

(ii) Where does the egg travel to?

_____ *1 mark*

(b) Complete the sentences below by filling in the two gaps.

The breakdown of the lining of the uterus is known as

_____ .

The complete 28 day series of changes is known as the

_____ . *2 marks*

(c) After fertilisation, the egg passes into the uterus and attaches itself to the lining.
(i) Why is the lining full of blood vessels?

_____

_____ *1 mark*

(ii) After about nine months the baby is born. How does the uterus help?

_____

_____ *1 mark*

Total Score [ ]

maximum 6 marks

4. Chris wanted to investigate physical and chemical changes. He put three different chemicals into separate test tubes. Each tube had a loose plug of mineral wool at the top. He weighed the tubes before and after heating, waiting until each tube was cold.

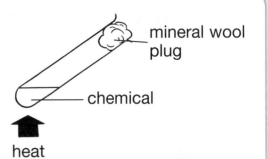

He recorded his observations in a table:

Experiment	Name of chemical	Observations	Change in mass
X	Calcium, a silver-coloured solid	Burned brightly with an orange flame, leaving a white solid	Increased
Y	Silicon dioxide, a yellow powder	Powder stayed as separate grains, still same colour at end	No change
Z	Potassium nitrate, white crystals	Solid melted then bubbled, went solid again on cooling	Decrease

(a) (i) In experiment X, the calcium reacted with one of the gases in the air.
Complete the word equation for the reaction of calcium in experiment X.

Calcium + _____ → _____   *2 marks*

(ii) Explain why the mass changed in experiment X.

_____

_____   *1 mark*

(b) What was the reason for using the mineral wool plug?

_____

_____   *1 mark*

(c) Name the yellow chemical left at the end in experiment Y.

_____   *1 mark*

(d) In each experiment, did a physical or a chemical change take place? Tick one box for each experiment.

experiment	chemical change	physical change
X	☐	☐
Y	☐	☐
Z	☐	☐

1 mark

Total Score ☐

maximum 6 marks

5. (a) The element bromine can be a solid, a liquid or a gas. Each change of state has its own name.

(i) The process of changing from solid to liquid is called

_____ .   *1 mark*

(ii) Liquid bromine is brown. At room temperature, a brown gas can be seen above the surface of liquid bromine. Explain why.

_____

_____   *2 marks*

(iii) Draw the arrangement of particles in bromine gas inside the box.

2 marks

(b) The boiling point of bromine is 59°C and its melting point is -7° Celsius.

(i) What is the physical state of bromine at 0°C?

_____   *1 mark*

(ii) Are the particles of bromine closer together at 0°C or at 60°C?

_____

_____   *2 marks*

Total Score

maximum 8 marks

48

6. Jo wanted to use four lamps to light a mirror on a dressing table. She worked out two ways to connect the lamps.

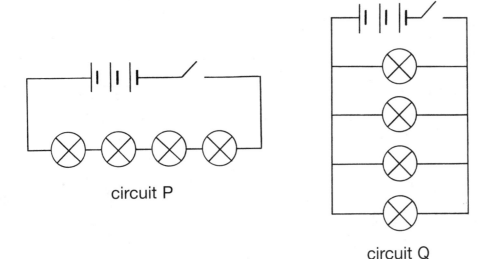

circuit P

circuit Q

(a) (i) One of the lamps was broken. Which circuit still worked with the other lamps shining? Explain why.

_____

_____ *2 marks*

(ii) What type of circuit is the one that did not work with the broken lamp?

_____ *1 mark*

(b) (i) Jo noticed that the lamps were hot to touch when they were switched on. Fill in the gaps to show the energy changes in the lamps.

Electrical energy _____ → _____ + _____ *2 marks*

(ii) What type of energy is being wasted?

_____ *1 mark*

Total Score ☐

maximum 6 marks

7. Al was investigating contact forces at the swimming pool.

slide

swimming pool

A friend timed how long each turn on the slide took. The results are shown in the table.

Experiment number	Conditions	Time in seconds
1	Dry slide and dry costume	8
2	Dry slide and wet costume	7
3	Water poured first on the slide	5

(a) What is the name of the contact force between the slide and the person sliding down?

_____ *1 mark*

(b) (i) What pattern do you notice in the results?

_____

_____ *2 marks*

(ii) What part is played by the water in this experiment?

_____ *1 mark*

Total Score ☐

maximum 4 marks

8. When you cut yourself, the wound usually bleeds. The blood soon forms a clot which hardens into a scab.

   (a) How does this help prevent infection by bacteria?

   _____

   _____ *1 mark*

   (b) (i) Bacteria may enter the body when you first cut yourself. Describe two responses made by white blood cells.

   _____

   _____

   _____

   _____ *2 marks*

   (ii) The body makes special proteins to attack bacteria. What are they called?

   _____ *1 mark*

   (c) Why do people rarely catch chicken-pox twice?

   _____

   _____ *2 marks*

Total Score ☐
maximum 6 marks

51

9. Mammoths became extinct about 10,000 years ago at the end of the last Ice Age. A number of well-preserved complete mammoths have been found deep frozen in the arctic.

(a) Why didn't the mammoths' bodies rot after they died?

_____

_____ *1 mark*

(b) (i) Some scientists want to extract genes (genetic information) from a frozen mammoth and use it to recreate the extinct animal. Suggest a living animal that is similar to a mammoth.

_____ *1 mark*

(ii) Scientists could combine genes from both types of animal and implant the fertilised egg. How might the baby animal resemble the two parents?

_____

_____ *2 marks*

Total Score ☐

maximum 4 marks

10. Marble is made of calcium carbonate. A cook noticed that a marble chopping board fizzed when vinegar was spilt on it. It left a permanent mark and a small hole. The cook found that the chemical reaction between marble and the vinegar fitted this pattern:

acid + carbonate → a salt + water + carbon dioxide

(a) Why did the marble board fizz?

_____

_____ *1 mark*

(b) (i) Would this reaction change the mass of the marble board?

_____

_____ *2 marks*

(ii) Marble statues that are left outside also change and are weathered. What can you deduce about the chemicals in rainwater from this observation?

_____

_____ *2 marks*

The cook wondered if other household materials might also react with marble. The results of some tests are shown in the table.

Material	pH value	Fizzing?
Fruit juice	4	Yes
Window cleaning liquid	9	No
Salt water	7	No
Material M	?	Yes, a lot

(c) What can you deduce about material M?

_____

_____ *2 marks*

Total Score

maximum 7 marks

11. Serena tried heating mixtures of metals and metal oxides together. She looked for any changes. The results are shown in the table.

Experiment number	Mixture	Observations
1	Grey iron + black copper oxide	Brown specks of copper
2	Grey iron metal + white zinc oxide	No changes
3	Grey zinc metal + brown iron oxide	Grey solid, attracted by a magnet

(a) Write a word equation for experiment 1.

_____   *2 marks*

(b) (i) Put the metals in order of reactivity.

Least reactive _____

Most reactive _____   *2 marks*

(ii) Calcium metal reacts with the oxides of all three metals in the table above. Where is calcium in this reactivity series?

_____   *1 mark*

Total Score

maximum 5 marks

12. Jack missed the school bus and decided to walk instead. The graph records his journey to school.

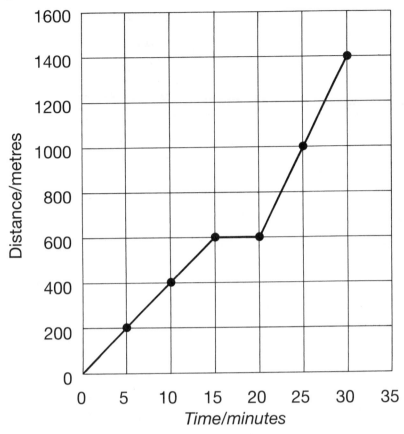

(a) It took Jack 30 minutes to reach school. How far away from home was the school?

_____ *1 mark*

(b) (i) Did Jack walk at a steady speed? Explain your answer.

_____

_____ *2 marks*

(ii) What was happening between 15 and 20 minutes?

_____ *1 mark*

(c) Calculate the average speed he was walking between 0 and 15 minutes.

_____

_____ *2 marks*

Total Score [ ]

maximum 6 marks

13. A parent took two young children to the playground to try out the seesaw.

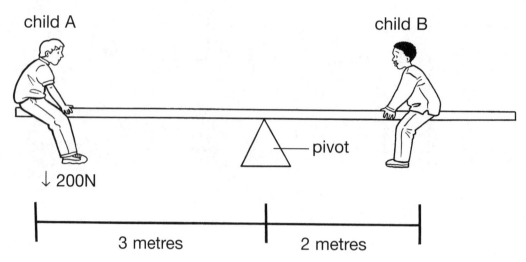

child A   child B

— pivot

↓ 200N

|← 3 metres →|← 2 metres →|

(a) Do the two children sitting at A and B have the same mass?
Explain your answer.

_____

_____   *2 marks*

(b) (i) What is the turning moment of the child at A?

_____

_____   *2 marks*

(ii) What is the downward force of the child at position B?

_____   *1 mark*

(c) If the child at A moved 1 metre closer to the pivot, how could
the child at B keep the seesaw in balance?

_____

_____   *1 mark*

Total Score

maximum 6 marks

Paper 2

Tier 5–7

- The test is 1 hour long.

- You will need: pen, pencil, rubber, ruler, protractor and calculator.

- The test starts with easier questions.

- Write all your answers on the test paper – do not use any rough paper.

- Check your work carefully.

- Ask your teacher if you are not sure what to do.

1. **(a)** Fran plays keyboard in a band.

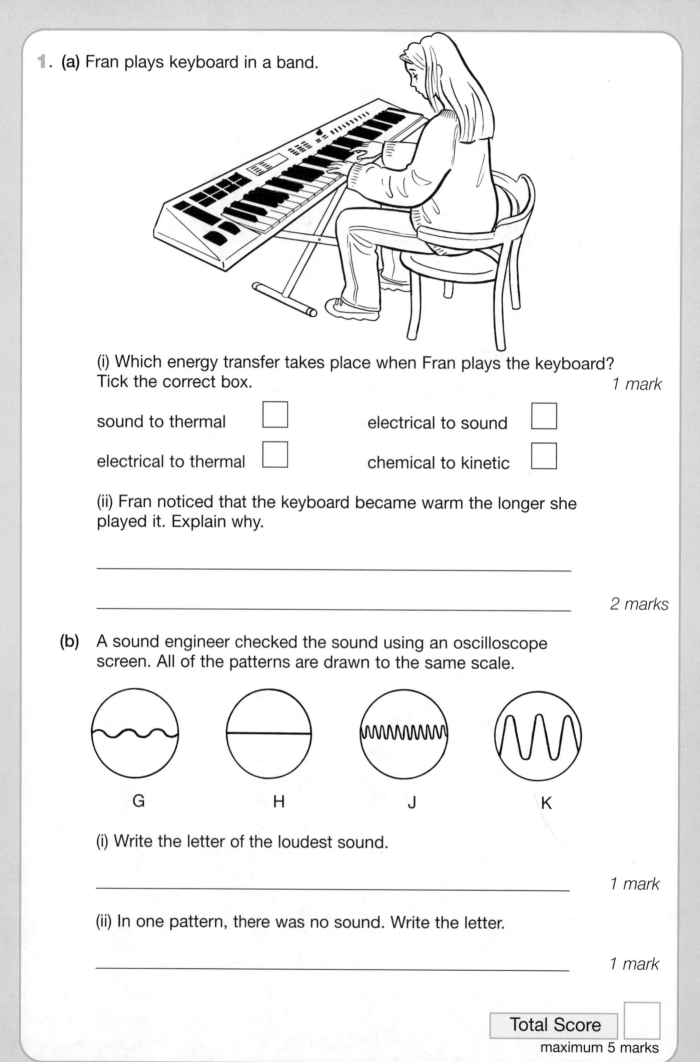

(i) Which energy transfer takes place when Fran plays the keyboard?
Tick the correct box.   *1 mark*

sound to thermal ☐   electrical to sound ☐

electrical to thermal ☐   chemical to kinetic ☐

(ii) Fran noticed that the keyboard became warm the longer she
played it. Explain why.

_____

_____ *2 marks*

(b) A sound engineer checked the sound using an oscilloscope
screen. All of the patterns are drawn to the same scale.

G   H   J   K

(i) Write the letter of the loudest sound.

_____ *1 mark*

(ii) In one pattern, there was no sound. Write the letter.

_____ *1 mark*

Total Score ☐
maximum 5 marks

58

2. Sunil is experimenting with a supermarket trolley.

(a)   (i) Name the downward force acting on the trolley.

_____   *1 mark*

(ii) Draw arrows on the diagram showing the **two** horizontal forces when Sunil is pushing the trolley along.   *2 marks*

(b)   Sunil lets go of the trolley on a downward slope. Explain what happens in terms of the forces acting on the trolley.

_____

_____   *2 marks*

(c)   The trolley crashes into a wall and stops. Explain what has happened to its kinetic energy.

_____

_____   *2 marks*

Total Score	

maximum 7 marks

3. The science of burning caused arguments for many years. Here are some observations about burning materials in air. One scientist predicted that when materials burn, they always weigh less afterwards.

Experiment number	Material burned	Observations + mass changes
1	Candle	Wax melted, candle became smaller, mass decreased
2	Magnesium ribbon	Formed a solid white ash, mass increased
3	Charcoal	Glowed red, left a grey ash, mass decreased
4	Iron filings	Sparkled, left a grey solid, mass increased

(a) Does this evidence support the original prediction? Explain your answer.

_____

_____ *2 marks*

(b) (i) In experiments 2 and 4 the product was a solid ash. In the other experiments, the products included gases. How could this help us understand the different mass changes?

_____

_____ *2 marks*

(ii) What further experiment needs to be done to see if the mass really falls or rises in experiment 1?

_____

_____ *1 mark*

Total Score

maximum 5 marks

4. Sara burned some hydrogen gas in a jet held just below a container of cold water.

(a) (i) Sara noticed that a liquid formed on the outside of the container. It was colourless and collected in the basin. Name this liquid.

_____ *1 mark*

(ii) The anhydrous (dried) copper sulphate turned from white to blue. Does this support your answer to part (i)?

_____

_____ *1 mark*

(b) (i) Explain why the flask was filled with cold water.

_____ *1 mark*

(ii) Containers of hydrogen have a hazard warning on them like this.

What does this sign mean?

_____ *1 mark*

(iii) Cylinders containing hydrogen gas should not be stored in direct sunlight. Explain why.

_____

_____ *2 marks*

Total Score [ ]

maximum 6 marks

5. Jack made saturated solutions of two chemicals at a range of temperatures. He found out how much solid had dissolved by weighing the tubes of solution each time. Here are the results. Solubility is measured in g of solid/kg water.

Chemical	0° Celsius	10	20	30	40	50	60	70
Potassium chloride	280	315	345	376	402	432	460	486
Sodium sulphate	45	92	210	412	482	464	450	438

(a) Jack decided to use the same size tube each time and the same volume of water. Explain why.

_____

_____ *2 marks*

(b) (i) What pattern do you see for the solution of potassium chloride?

_____ *1 mark*

(ii) How does sodium sulphate compare?

_____

_____ *1 mark*

Total Score ☐

maximum 4 marks

6. The diagrams show cells from plants.

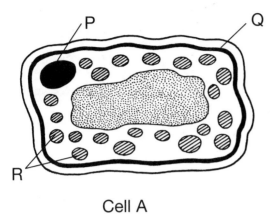

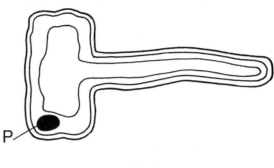

Cell A   Cell

(a) Letter P is the control centre for the cell.

We call it the _____ .   *1 mark*

(b) (i) What part of the cell is Q?

_____   *1 mark*

(ii) One of the cells takes part in photosynthesis. It is cell _____ .

The reason for this choice of answer is that _____

_____ .   *1 mark*

(c) (i) Complete the word equation for photosynthesis:

_____ _____ + water ⟶ glucose + _____
                          light and a
                          green pigment   *2 marks*

(ii) Name the green pigment.

_____   *1 mark*

Total Score ☐

maximum 6 marks

63

7. A balanced diet is essential to maintain good health. Part of this diet should be minerals and vitamins.

Mineral	Not enough of it	Foods that contain it
Calcium	Weak bones, teeth	Milk, green vegetables
Iron	Unhealthy blood cells (anaemia)	Meat, nuts
Sodium	Muscle cramps	Salt
Vitamin A	Poor eyesight, skin problems	Milk, butter, carrots
Vitamin C	Bleeding gums, loose teeth (scurvy)	Lemons, oranges, tomatoes

(a) Name a source of iron in the diet.

_____   *1 mark*

(b) (i) Some people do not eat meat. How can they obtain the iron they need?

_____   *1 mark*

(ii) Two hundred years ago, before the invention of fridges or tinned food, sailors could not obtain enough fresh fruit or vegetables on long voyages. What health problems might this cause?

_____

_____   *2 marks*

(c) Which mineral is needed for strong bones?

_____   *1 mark*

Total Score [ ]

maximum 5 marks

8. Colours can look different in daylight and in artificial light.

The colours of the spotlight keep changing. One dancer's sweatshirt looks like this:

Spotlight colour	Sweatshirt looked
red	red
blue	blue
green	green

(a) What colour is the sweatshirt in daylight? Explain your answer.

_____

_____ *2 marks*

(b) (i) Another dancer's shirt looked green in daylight but black in a blue spotlight. Explain why.

_____

_____ *2 marks*

(ii) In clothes shops some customers ask to take the clothes near a window or door before buying them. Explain why.

_____ *1 mark*

Total Score ☐

maximum 5 marks

9. When rocks underground get very hot, they can melt. When molten material cools, it forms new rock.

(a) The name of this type of new rock is _____ .   *1 mark*

(b) Jess wanted to know if the sizes of the crystals in the rocks was linked to the way that they cooled. Jess melted some salol crystals and let them cool down.

crystals

hot liquid cooled slowly   hot liquid cooled quickly

(i) What is the difference between the two sets of crystalline samples?

_____   *1 mark*

(ii) Explain why they are different.

_____

_____   *2 marks*

(c) Lava from a volcano cools quickly and turns into new solid rock. What could you predict about the crystals in lava rock, based on the experiment?

_____

_____   *1 mark*

Total Score

maximum 5 marks

66

10. A young child was playing with a toy crane that had a magnet instead of a hook.

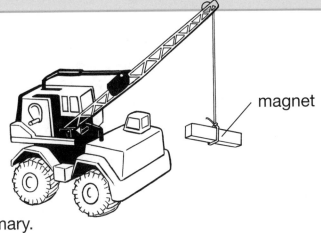

toy crane

magnet

The child found that some things stuck to the magnet. Here is a summary.

Object	Effect of the magnet
Iron nail	Stuck to magnet
Copper coin	No effect
Paper clips	Stuck
Copper coloured drawing pin	Stuck

(a) Which result or results are unexpected?

_____

_____ *2 marks*

(b) (i) The child found that the objects which stuck to the magnet remained in place. They had to be pulled off to remove them. Explain why.

_____ *1 mark*

(ii) The child's mother made an electromagnet to replace the ordinary bar magnet on the crane.

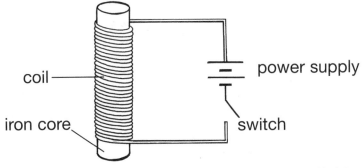

coil

iron core

power supply

switch

The magnetism could be switched on or off this time. Explain how this kind of magnet works.

_____

_____ *2 marks*

Total Score

maximum 5 marks

67

11. Cara tested samples of different metals with acids. In each case she placed a 1cm square piece of the metal in a tube containing 5ml of the acid. Here are the results. A cross (x) shows that no reaction was seen.

Metals	Calcium	Magnesium	Lead	Copper
Acids used				
Hydrochloric acid	very fast, bubbles	fast, bubbles	a few bubbles	X
Citric acid	quite fast, bubbles	slow, bubbles	X	X
Sulphuric acid	very fast, bubbles, then slowed down	fast, bubbles	X	X

(a) (i) Which is the least reactive metal tested?

_____ *1 mark*

(ii) This metal is used in car radiators and for water pipes. Give a reason for choosing this metal.

_____ *1 mark*

(b) (i) Vinegar contains an acid of similar strength to citric acid. How will vinegar react with magnesium?

_____ *1 mark*

(ii) Metals react with acids to form salts such as calcium sulphate. Calcium sulphate is insoluble. How does this explain the reaction of calcium with sulphuric acid?

_____

_____ *2 marks*

(c) (i) Complete the word equation.

magnesium + _____ _____ → magnesium sulphate + hydrogen

1 mark

(ii) Using the evidence in the table, which is the weakest acid?

_____ *1 mark*

Total Score ☐

maximum 7 marks

12. Some people say that plants grow differently in light of different colours. Imagine that you are planning a laboratory investigation to test this idea: 'the colour of light affects how plants grow'.

Assume you have access to any laboratory apparatus you need, including:
- lamps with red or green bulbs
- seeds
- seed trays
- soil

(a) Name a factor you would need to vary in your investigation. (This is the independent variable.)

_____ *1 mark*

(b) (i) What factor would you examine to see any effect? (This is the dependent variable.)

_____ *1 mark*

(ii) How could you measure the dependent variable?

_____ *1 mark*

(c) Suggest one factor you would control to ensure that your investigation was a fair test.

_____

_____ *1 mark*

Total Score	

maximum 4 marks

13. (a) Insoluble salts can be made by mixing together solutions of two soluble salts.

(i) Complete the word equation.

potassium chloride solution + _____ _____ solution

      → lead chloride solid + potassium nitrate solution

2 marks

(ii) How could the insoluble lead chloride be separated?

_____

1 mark

(b) Metal oxides are examples of bases. There is a general reaction:

acid + base _____ → a salt + water

Name the base you need to make zinc sulphate from sulphuric acid.

_____

1 mark

(c) In the table below, write the name of the compound represented by each formula.

Formula	Name of compound
$CaCl_2$	
$FeSO_4$	

2 marks

Total Score

maximum 6 marks

14. A group of pupils investigated the time it took for a mixture of solutions to turn cloudy.

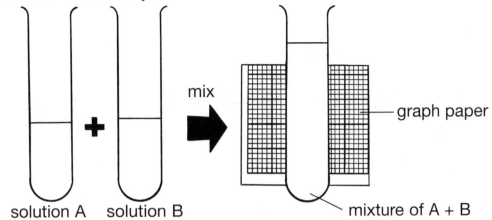

solution A   solution B   mix   graph paper   mixture of A + B

In each case, solutions A and B were mixed and held in front of some graph paper. The time was measured from mixing until the cloudiness stopped the pupils seeing the squares on the graph paper. A range of temperatures was used and the solutions were warmed before mixing.

Temperature/°C	Time/seconds	Time/s first repeat	Time/s second repeat
0	200	210	205
10	110	105	105
20	60	65	60
30	36	39	62
40	20	22	25
50	12	13	10
60	8	7	6
70	5	4	4
80	2	3	1

(a) One pupil concluded that there was one result that was clearly wrong. Which one?

_____   *1 mark*

(b) Another pupil said that since they used the same clock, all of the times are equally reliable. Is this correct?

_____

_____   *2 marks*

(c) (i) Give one other way in which this data could be displayed to make spotting errors easier.

_____   *1 mark*

(ii) What conclusion can you draw from these results?

_____   *1 mark*

Total Score

maximum 5 marks

15.(a) Sophie noticed that her desk lamp was very hot to touch. Complete the energy transfer equation:

electricity ➔ _____ + _____   *2 marks*

(b) When she changed to using a low energy bulb, the light was equally bright but the lamp was only slightly warm. Explain why.

_____

_____   *2 marks*

(c) The markings on the two lamps were different. The ordinary filament lamp was 100W but the low energy lamp was marked 20W. Why is this good both for Sophie and for the environment?

_____

_____   *2 marks*

Total Score

maximum 6 marks

Answers and tips

Paper 1

Tier 3–6

1. (a) 1 **strong legs** are needed to do heavy work and pull the plough.
2 **calm nature** since horses must work together in a ploughing team.
Answers can be the other way round.   *4 marks*

(b) Father's **sperm** contains the (genetic) information that makes the foal resemble its father.   *1 mark*

(c) The foals are not identical, even though the parents are the same, as with brothers and sisters.   *1 mark*

Total 6 Marks

2. (a) The bars should be labelled from left to right:
A ants   C flies   D slugs   B snails   *3 marks*

> **Tip:** Note that in this question you need 4 correct answers for 3 marks. Look out for this in examination papers.

(b) The hedgehog eats the slugs, leaving less food for the bird. The bird might hunt for food somewhere else in future.   *2 marks*

(c) The ant and fly killer reduces the food available to other wildlife, such as birds. The spray may also poison other wildlife in the garden.   *2 marks*

Total 7 Marks

3. (a) Air (or oxygen) and water are needed   *2 marks*

(b) Temperature was the variable here.   *1 mark*

(c) The tube is dry; seeds need water to grow.   *1 mark*

(d) Light, since the aluminium foil will cut out the light and stop it reaching the seeds.   *1 mark*

Total 5 Marks

4. (a) A is the filter funnel which supports the paper.
B is the filter paper which separates solids from liquid.
C is the filtrate (or the solution) which goes through the paper.
Note that in this question you need 3 correct answers for
2 marks.   *2 marks*

> **Tip:** Learn the names of common pieces of equipment as they are often included.

(b) (i) Sawdust is insoluble (cannot dissolve) and so can be filtered off. The others are soluble (can dissolve) and so go through the filter paper unchanged. *1 mark*

(ii) Sand is insoluble and will be trapped in the filter paper. *1 mark*

(c) Distil the seawater and collect the pure water as the steam condenses. *1 mark*

Total 5 Marks

5. (a) Q was probably a metal since it was shiny and conducts electricity. *2 marks*

(b) All metals **conduct heat**. Not all are silvery in colour – think about brown copper. Mercury is a liquid metal. *1 mark*

(c) Use a magnet since steel (made of iron) is magnetic but aluminium is not. *1 mark*

(d) Copper reacts with oxygen in the air when it is heated; it forms black copper oxide. *2 marks*

 There are only two liquid elements so it is useful to remember them: metallic mercury and the non-metal liquid bromine.

Total 6 Marks

6. (a) (i) Paraffin since the temperature rises the most. *1 mark*

(ii) Carbon dioxide because all three fuels contain carbon which burns to form carbon dioxide. *1 mark*

(b) (i) Ethanol has a clear blue flame and there is no smoke or soot. *1 mark*

(c) Renewable fuels will not run out; we can produce more of them. For example, we can grow sugar beet, extract the sugar and turn it into alcohol for use as a fuel. *2 marks*

 Gas test results are favourite questions. You need to remember tests for oxygen, hydrogen and carbon dioxide.

Total 5 Marks

7. (a) The curved Earth gives a curved shadow on the Moon, just like the shadow of a ball on a wall. Sunlight travels in straight lines, just like other forms of radiation. *2 marks*

(b) The Moon is in orbit round the Earth and quickly moves out of the Earth's shadow so ending the eclipse. *2 marks*

(c) You cannot see the Sun at all from the Moon during a lunar eclipse; it is blocked out by the Earth. *1 mark*

 Tip: Planets and the moon are seen by reflected light. Remember that only stars, like the Sun, produce their own light.

Total 5 Marks

8. (a) The fastest is aluminium at 5000m/s. *1 mark*

(b) (i) We do not need the **speed of light in air** for this experiment. For short distances light travels too fast to measure its speed (300 million metres/second). *1 mark*

(ii) Sam needs to repeat experiment B since it is very different from the others, suggesting that there might be an error. *2 marks*

 Tip: Remember that the order for the speed of sound is: fastest in solids, next in liquids and slowest in gases.

Total 4 Marks

9. (a) Light travels much faster than sound in air and so the noise arrives later than the flash of light. *2 marks*

(b) (i) Observer C was closest since the noise arrived in the shortest time. *1 mark*

(ii) B was 7.0 seconds and F was 14.0 seconds, that is 7 seconds more or double the time. So H is half-way and it will take 7.0 to reach B plus 3.5 more to reach observer H = 10.5 seconds. *2 marks*

Total 5 Marks

10. (a) Draw a line from 'sunlight' to 'to run the fridge'; it uses solar cells to change light into electricity.
Draw a line from 'flowing water' to 'to cook food' since the water powers the turbine making electricity for the cooker. *2 marks*

 Tip: Always draw lines first for the answers you are certain are correct. Guess the others from what is left over.

(b) (i) Less water flowing means that the turbine produces less electricity for the cooker, perhaps not enough for it to work at all. *1 mark*

(ii) The trees and bushes could be used for firewood for cooking. This is a renewable source of energy.   *1 mark*

Total 4 Marks

11. (a) The rib cage   *1 mark*

(b) (i) the humerus is **A**   *1 mark*
(ii) the femur is **C**   *1 mark*
(iii) the collar bone is **B**   *1 mark*

(c) The knee joint is like a hinge – the bones can move backwards and forwards. It cannot move in any other direction, such as sideways.   *1 mark*

(d) The cartilage is a coating on the ends of the bones. Since it is smooth, the hinge moves freely.   *1 mark*

Total 6 Marks

12. (a) (i) the windpipe is **Z**   *1 mark*
(ii) alveoli are **Y**   *1 mark*

(b) (i) On the surface of the alveoli is where gases can be exchanged.   *1 mark*
(ii) Carbon monoxide is poisonous and reduces the amount of oxygen carried by the blood.   *1 mark*

(c) Carbon monoxide in the blood reduces the amount of oxygen it can carry round the body. Less oxygen means that the athlete's muscles will not work so well.   *2 marks*

 Tip: Questions about smoking are common. Make sure you know about the dangers of tar and of carbon monoxide.

Total 6 Marks

13. (a) (i) Day 14 is when the egg is released.   *1 mark*
(ii) It travels to the uterus   *1 mark*

(b) The breakdown of the lining of the uterus is known as **menstruation**.
The complete 28 day series of changes is known as the **menstruation cycle**.   *2 marks*

(c) (i) Blood vessels are needed as the embryo develops into a baby, to supply its food and oxygen supply.   *1 mark*
(ii) The walls of the uterus contract and push the baby out.   *1 mark*

Total 6 Marks

14. (a) (i) calcium + **oxygen** → **calcium oxide** (this is an
oxidation reaction) *2 marks*
(ii) Calcium combined with oxygen so the mass went up. *1 mark*

(b) The mineral wool stops any solid leaving the tube and
changing the mass. The wool lets air in and any gases
out of the tube. *1 mark*

(c) Silicon dioxide since no change had occurred on heating. *1 mark*

(d)

experiment	chemical change	physical change	
X	✓		
Y		✓	
Z	✓		*1 mark*

> **Tip:** Remember the composition of the air: 78% unreactive nitrogen, 21%
> reactive oxygen and 1% for the rest.

Total 6 Marks

15. (a) (i) Melting *1 mark*
(ii) Liquid bromine is evaporating at room temperature to
give brown bromine gas. *2 marks*
(iii)

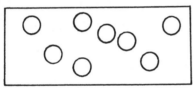

2 marks

1 mark for separate particles / 1 mark for random pattern.

> **Tip:** Check you can draw and recognise particle patterns for solids,
> liquids and gases.

(b) (i) Bromine is a liquid at 0° Celsius since it is above the
melting point but below the boiling point. *1 mark*

(ii) Bromine is a liquid at 0° Celsius and at 60° Celsius
it is a gas. The particles are closer together in liquids
than in gases. *2 marks*

Total 8 Marks

16. **(a)** (i) Circuit Q still worked because in parallel circuits there is still a complete circuit even when one lamp is broken. The electricity has more than one possible pathway. *2 marks*
(ii) The series circuit, because the electricity has to move first through one component then through the next and so on. *1 mark*

> Tip: Follow the path of electricity right round the series circuit. If there is a break, then it won't work.

(b) (i) Electrical energy → **heat + light** *2 marks*
(ii) Heat is wasted since the lamp is needed to give out light. *1 mark*

Total 6 Marks

17. **(a)** Friction *1 mark*

(b) (i) The more wet it is, the less time it takes. *2 marks*
(ii) Water acts as a lubricant; it reduces the friction and lets the person slide more quickly. *1 mark*

Total 4 Marks

Total marks on this paper = 94 marks

Paper 2

Tier 3–6

1. (a) The force of gravity acts downwards towards the Earth, so tick the downward arrow.   *1 mark*

   (b) Gravity will cause it to move downwards.   *1 mark*

   (c) The forces are balanced, this is why it moves at a constant speed.   *1 mark*

   > **Tip:** Remember the rule that when forces are balanced, an object stays still or moves at a steady speed.

   (d) The tear in the fabric will reduce the air resistance. This will make the parachute fall more quickly when it is released.   *2 marks*

   Total 5 Marks

2. (a) Venus and the Earth are similar sizes and similar masses. Venus is closer to the Sun and so it experiences a greater pull of gravity.   *2 marks*

   (b) (i) The Earth orbits the Sun once a year and so in 76 years it will orbit 76 times.   *1 mark*
   (ii) It takes 24 hours or one day, for the Earth to rotate on its axis.   *1 mark*

   > **Tip:** Only on Earth is the year 365 days. Year lengths on other planets are different.

   Total 4 Marks

3. (a) (i) Fossil fuels are the remains of living things from long ago; for example, coal comes from the remains of ancient plants.   *1 mark*
   (ii) Coal is the most difficult to transport since it is a solid. Liquids and gases are easier to move, for example by pipeline.   *2 marks*

   (b) Carbon dioxide is released by burning fossil fuels and it may be responsible for global warming.   *1 mark*

   (c) (i) Sulphur dioxide reacts with air and moisture to produce acid rain (sulphuric acid).   *1 mark*

   > **Tip:** Acid rain also contains nitric acid from nitrogen oxides produced in car engines.

(ii) Solar energy uses the Sun's heat and light and does
not release any polluting gases such as carbon dioxide.
It cannot cause global warming.

1 mark

Total 6 Marks

4. **(a)** To make it a fair test you must have equal amounts of
nail polish each time.

1 mark

 Tip: Check you understand the meaning of a fair test. Think about
investigations you have carried out.

(b) The cotton wool would go red as some polish was
removed. The blob of polish would get smaller or be
removed completely.

1 mark

(c) The best nail polish remover would:
• clean the slide most easily
• not evaporate too fast.

2 marks

Total 4 Marks

5. **(a)** The corks all point to the magnetic north pole, just like
compass needles.

1 mark

(b) Opposite magnetic poles attract, so the north pole of
one needle magnet attracts the south pole of the next.

1 mark

(c) Like poles repel so the needlepoint must have been a
north pole as well.

1 mark

(d) Copper is not a magnetic metal and cannot be magnetised
with a bar magnet.

1 mark

Total 4 Marks

6. **(a)** The chalk is bubbling in the acid and a gas is collecting
in the gas jar.

2 marks

Tip: Changes in chemical reactions include heat, colour, gases and ash

(b) (i) It is not soluble or not very soluble in water since it
bubbles through water and collects in the jar.

1 mark

(ii) The gas in the bottle is under pressure, this makes it
more soluble in the water.

1 mark

(c) The order is:
nitrogen (most)   oxygen   carbon dioxide (least)

1 mark

Total 5 Marks

7. **(a)** Sedimentary rocks can contain fossils, such as limestone or sandstone. *1 mark*

(b) Rock B is a metamorphic rock. The original sedimentary rock, as at A, has been changed by heat and pressure caused by the volcano. *2 marks*

(c) (i) Rock C cooled underground, slowly enough for large crystals to form. At D, the heat escaped quickly at the surface and smaller crystals formed as the liquid turned to a solid more rapidly. *2 marks*

(ii) Rocks C and D are both igneous rocks since both were formed from hot molten magma. *1 mark*

> **Tip:** Make sure you can describe the main differences between sedimentary, metamorphic and igneous rocks.

(d) Nothing could live inside a volcano owing to the high temperatures. Even if animal or plant remains fell in, the heat would destroy them. *1 mark*

Total 7 Marks

8. **(a)** **A** Slug – **mollusc**, soft body, no backbone
B Honey bee – **insect**
C Dog – **mammal**, warm-blooded, with a backbone
D Crab – **crustacean**, most live in water, external skeleton, no backbone *4 marks*

(b) The dog (**C**) is the only vertebrate (has a backbone). *1 mark*

Total 5 Marks

9. **(a)** 1. **Good conductor of electricity**
2. **Flexible**, wires need to bend without breaking.
(These answers can be the other way round) *2 marks*

(b) (i) Mercury has a low melting point and so it is a liquid at room temperature. *1 mark*

(ii) Aluminium is strong and holds the glass firmly in place. *1 mark*

> **Tip:** Make a checklist of the properties of metals and of non-metals and learn it.

Total 4 Marks

10. **(a)** (i) **electrical to sound**; the mains electricity is changed into musical sounds. *1 mark*

   (b) (ii) Some of the electrical energy was wasted (1 mark) as heat (1 mark). The energy transfer was not 100% efficient, hence the waste heat. *2 marks*

  (b) (i) The loudest sound is **K**; the wave shows the greatest movement up and down and this is called the greatest amplitude. *1 mark*

    (ii) There is no sound in **H**; the oscilloscope trace just shows it going across the screen unchanged. *1 mark*

Total 5 Marks

11. **(a)** (i) The downward force here is gravity which pulls everything down towards the Earth. *1 mark*

    (ii) The arrows show the smaller force of friction and the larger force from Sunil pushing. *2 marks*

Tip: Arrows to show forces tell us two things: the direction and the size of the force.

  (b) On the downward slope, the force of gravity makes the trolley speed up (accelerate). The forward force increases and the reverse frictional force is much less than the forward force. *2 marks*

  (c) The kinetic energy is converted into other forms of energy such as sound, heat and the energy used to dent the trolley and the wall. *2 marks*

Total 7 Marks

12. (a) No, some masses increase and others decrease. *2 marks*

(b) (i) We can weigh the ash for experiments 2 and 4. For experiments 1 and 3 the gases formed just escape into the air and we cannot weigh them. We cannot tell if the mass went up or down in experiments 1 and 3. *2 marks*
(ii) We need to trap or collect the gases in experiment 1 and weigh them, together with the weight of the candle that is left. Only then can we tell if the mass fell or increased. *1 mark*

Total 5 Marks

13. (a) (i) The liquid was water. *1 mark*
(ii) Yes, this is one of the tests for water or liquids that contain water such as lemonade. *1 mark*

(b) (i) The steam produced by the hydrogen flame condensed on the cold surface of the flask to give water. *1 mark*

Tip: Remember that the full name for water is hydrogen oxide.

(ii) The sign means flammable; hydrogen/air mixtures can catch fire and explode. *1 mark*
(iii) The cylinder would get hot, the gas inside would expand and the pressure would increase. It could start leaking and cause an explosion. *2 marks*

Total 6 Marks

14. (a) To make it a fair test we must keep all of the conditions the same except one. In this case, that one is the temperature. *2 marks*

(b) (i) The higher the temperature, the higher the solubility. *1 mark*
(ii) The solubility of sodium sulphate is unusual. It rises up to 40°C then falls as the temperature rises further. *1 mark*

Tip: Saturated solutions are full of solute; nothing more can dissolve.

Total 4 Marks

15. (a) The control centre is the **cell nucleus**. *1 mark*

(b) (i) Q is the **cell wall**; it is quite thick in plant cells. *1 mark*
(ii) It is cell **A**. The reason is that cell A contains chloroplasts which contain chlorophyll, needed for photosynthesis. *1 mark*

(c) (i) **carbon dioxide** + water → glucose + **oxygen**
$$\text{light and a green pigment}$$
2 marks
(ii) The green pigment is called **chlorophyll**. *1 mark*

Total 6 Marks

16. (a) Iron is contained in meat and in nuts. *1 mark*

(b) (i) Eat nuts instead of meat, since they contain iron as well. *1 mark*
(ii) No fresh fruit or vegetables means that their diet lacks vitamin C. They could suffer from scurvy with bleeding gums and loose teeth. *2 marks*

(c) **Calcium** is the mineral needed for strong bones and for teeth. *1 mark*

Total 5 Marks

17. (a) The sweatshirt must be **white** in daylight since it reflects all other colours equally well. *2 marks*

(b) (i) The green shirt reflects the green part of daylight. It absorbs blue and red light. So in a blue spotlight, the blue is absorbed. No light is reflected and it looks black. *2 marks*
(ii) The colours of the clothes look different in daylight, i.e. near the window or door. It is a good idea to check the colour before buying. *1 mark*

> Tip: Remember that coloured dyes in fabrics absorb all colours except the colour you can see.

Total 5 Marks

Total marks on this paper = 87 marks

Paper 1

Tier 5–7

1. (a) The rib cage *1 mark*

(b) (i) the humerus is **A** *1 mark*
(ii) the femur is **C** *1 mark*
(iii) the collar bone is **B** *1 mark*

(c) The knee joint is like a hinge – the bones can move backwards and forwards. It cannot move in any other direction, such as sideways. *1 mark*

(d) The cartilage is a coating on the ends of the bones. Since it is smooth, the hinge moves freely. *1 mark*

Total 6 Marks

2. (a) (i) the windpipe is **Z** *1 mark*
(ii) alveoli are **Y** *1 mark*

(b) (i) On the surface of the alveoli is where gases can be exchanged. *1 mark*
(ii) Carbon monoxide is poisonous and reduces the amount of oxygen carried by the blood. *1 mark*

(c) Carbon monoxide in the blood reduces the amount of oxygen it can carry round the body. Less oxygen means that the athlete's muscles will not work so well. *2 marks*

Tip: Questions about smoking are common. Make sure you know about the dangers of tar and of carbon monoxide.

Total 6 Marks

3. (a) (i) Day 14 is when the egg is released. *1 mark*
(iii) It travels to the uterus *1 mark*

(b) The breakdown of the lining of the uterus is known as menstruation.
The complete 28 day series of changes is known as the menstruation cycle. *2 marks*

(c) (i) Blood vessels are needed as the embryo develops into a baby, to supply its food and oxygen supply. *1 mark*
(ii) The walls of the uterus contract and push the baby out. *1 mark*

Total 6 Marks

4. **(a)** (i) calcium + **oxygen** → **calcium oxide**
(this is an oxidation reaction)   *2 marks*
(ii) Calcium combined with oxygen so the mass went up.   *1 mark*

(b) The mineral wool stops any solid leaving the tube and
changing the mass. The wool lets air in and any gases
out of the tube.   *1 mark*

(c) Silicon dioxide since no change had occurred on heating.   *1 mark*

(d)
experiment	chemical change	physical change
X	✓	
Y		✓
Z	✓	

1 mark

> **Tip:** Remember the composition of the air: 78% unreactive nitrogen, 21% reactive oxygen and 1% for the rest.

Total 6 Marks

5. **(a)** (i) Melting   *1 mark*
(ii) Liquid bromine is evaporating at room temperature to
give brown bromine gas.   *2 marks*
(iii)

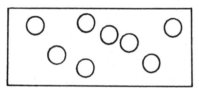

2 marks

1 mark for separate particles / 1 mark for random pattern.

> **Tip:** Check you can draw and recognise particle patterns for solids, liquids and gases.

(b) (i) Bromine is a liquid at 0° Celsius since it is above the
melting point but below the boiling point.   *1 mark*
(iii) Bromine is a liquid at 0° Celsius and at 60° Celsius
it is a gas. The particles are closer together in liquids
than in gases.   *2 marks*

Total 8 Marks

6. **(a)** (i) Circuit Q still worked because in parallel circuits there is still a complete circuit even when one lamp is broken. The electricity has more than one possible pathway. *2 marks*

(ii) The series circuit, because the electricity has to move first through one component then through the next and so on. *1 mark*

> **Tip:** Follow the path of electricity right round the series circuit. If there is a break, then it won't work.

(b) (i) Electrical energy → **heat** + **light** *2 marks*

(ii) Heat is wasted since the lamp is needed to give out light. *1 mark*

Total 6 Marks

7. **(a)** Friction *1 mark*

(b) (i) The more wet it is, the less time it takes. *2 marks*

(ii) Water acts as a lubricant; it reduces the friction and lets the person slide more quickly. *1 mark*

Total 4 Marks

8. **(a)** The scab seals the hole in the skin so keeping bacteria out. *1 mark*

(b) (i) White blood cells move towards the cut (1 mark) and attack bacteria and kill them (1 mark). *2 marks*

(ii) **Antibodies**; they stick to the bacteria and allow the body to destroy them more easily. *1 mark*

(c) Once you have been infected with chicken pox, the antibodies can be produced again more easily than the first time. *2 marks*

Total 6 Marks

9. **(a)** Low temperature preserves meat and stops it going bad. This is why we use freezers. *1 mark*

> **Tip:** The clue to this answer is in the question – 'deep frozen'. Read all questions carefully.

(b) (i) Elephants are similar to Mammoths.

1 mark

(ii) The baby would have characteristics of each; for example, mammoths have body hair and elephants have different smaller tusks.

2 marks

Total 4 Marks

10.(a) The calcium carbonate reacted with the vinegar to give a gas.

1 mark

> **Tip:** This is one of the few general chemical reactions. Make a checklist of others you have used.

(b) (i) Some of the marble is converted to a gas which then escapes into the air. The mass decreases since gases have a mass like everything else.

2 marks

(ii) Rain water must contain an acid (1 mark) that reacts with the marble in the statue in the same way as the marble board (1 mark).

2 marks

(c) Material M is acidic (1 mark) and is a stronger acid than fruit juice, less than pH 4 (1 mark).

2 marks

Total 7 Marks

11.(a) Iron + copper oxide → iron oxide + copper (1 mark for each side)

2 marks

(b) (i) Least reactive is **copper**. Most reactive is **zinc**.

2 marks

(ii) Calcium is the most reactive, therefore it goes below zinc in the series.

1 mark

> **Tip:** Make sure you understand how the reactivity series of metals works. It is very useful for many questions.

Total 5 Marks

12. (a) In 30 minutes, he travelled 1400 metres (check the graph).   *1 mark*

(b) (i) Jack varied his speed as shown by the different
gradients (slopes) of the line.   *2 marks*
(ii) Jack stopped moving; no extra distance was travelled
between these times.   *1 mark*

(c) Between 0 and 15 minutes he walked 600 metres.

Average speed $= \dfrac{\text{distance}}{\text{time}} = \dfrac{600}{15} = 40$ metres/minute   *2 marks*

Tip: Try drawing some distance-time graphs of your own to check your
understanding.

Total 6 Marks

13. (a) No, child B must be heavier (has a larger mass). They
can balance the seesaw sitting closer to the pivot.   *2 marks*

(b) (i) Turning moment = force x distance from the pivot
= 200N x 3m
= 600Nm = Turning moment of child at A   *2 marks*
(ii) Since the seesaw is in balance,
600Nm = force by child at B x 2metres
so force by child at B = 300N   *1 mark*

(c) Child at B also moves towards the pivot to maintain
the balance.   *1 mark*

Total 6 Marks

Total marks on this paper = 76 marks

Paper 2

Tier 5–7

1. **(a)** (i) **electrical to sound**; the mains electricity is changed into musical sounds.

1 mark

(ii) Some of the electrical energy was wasted (1 mark) as heat (1 mark). The energy transfer was not 100% efficient, hence the waste heat.

2 marks

(b) (i) The loudest sound is **K**; the wave shows the greatest movement up and down and this is called the greatest amplitude.

1 mark

(ii) There is no sound in **H**; the oscilloscope trace just shows it going across the screen unchanged.

1 mark

Total 5 Marks

2. **(a)** (i) The downward force here is gravity which pulls everything down towards the Earth.

1 mark

(ii) The arrows will show the smaller force of friction and the larger force from Sunil pushing.

2 marks

> **Tip:** Arrows to show forces tell us two things: the direction and the size of the force.

(b) On the downward slope, the force of gravity makes the trolley speed up (accelerate). The forward force increases and the reverse frictional force is much less than the forward force.

2 marks

90

(c) The kinetic energy is converted into other forms of energy such as sound, heat and the energy used to dent the trolley and the wall. *2 marks*

Total 7 Marks

3. (a) No, some masses increase and others decrease. *2 marks*

(b) (i) We can weigh the ash for experiments 2 and 4. For experiments 1 and 3 the gases formed just escape into the air and we cannot weigh them. We cannot tell if the mass went up or down in experiments 1 and 3. *2 marks*
(ii) We need to trap or collect the gases in experiment 1 and weigh them, together with the weight of the candle that is left. Only then can we tell if the mass fell or increased. *1 mark*

Total 5 Marks

4. (a) (i) The liquid was water. *1 mark*
(ii) Yes, this is one of the tests for water or liquids that contain water such as lemonade. *1 mark*

(b) (i) The steam produced by the hydrogen flame condensed on the cold surface of the flask to give water. *1 mark*

> **Tip:** Remember that the full name for water is hydrogen oxide.

(ii) The sign means flammable; hydrogen/air mixtures can catch fire and explode. *1 mark*
(iii) The cylinder would get hot, the gas inside would expand and the pressure would increase. It could start leaking and cause an explosion. *2 marks*

Total 6 Marks

5. (a) To make it a fair test we must keep all of the conditions the same except one. In this case, that one is the temperature. *2 marks*

(b) (i) The higher the temperature, the higher the solubility. *1 mark*
(ii) The solubility of sodium sulphate is unusual. It rises up to 40°C then falls as the temperature rises further. *1 mark*

> **Tip:** Saturated solutions are full of solute; nothing more can dissolve.

Total 4 Marks

6. **(a)** The control centre is the **cell nucleus**. *1 mark*

(b) (i) Q is the **cell wall**; it is quite thick in plant cells. *1 mark*
(ii) It is cell **A**. The reason is that cell A contains chloroplasts which contain chlorophyll, needed for photosynthesis. *1 mark*

(c) (i) **carbon dioxide** + water $\rightarrow$ glucose + **oxygen**
light and a
green pigment *2 marks*
(ii) The green pigment is called **chlorophyll**. *1 mark*

Total 6 Marks

7. **(a)** Iron is contained in meat and in nuts. *1 mark*

(b) (i) Eat nuts instead of meat, since they contain iron as well. *1 mark*

(ii) No fresh fruit or vegetables means that their diet lacks vitamin C. They could suffer from scurvy with bleeding gums and loose teeth. *2 marks*

(c) **Calcium** is the mineral needed for strong bones and for teeth. *1 mark*

Total 5 Marks

8. **(a)** The sweatshirt must be **white** in daylight since it reflects all other colours equally well. *2 marks*

(b) (i) The green shirt reflects the green part of daylight. It absorbs blue and red light. So in a blue spotlight, the blue is absorbed. No light is reflected and it looks black. *2 marks*
(ii) The colours of the clothes look different in daylight, i.e. near the window or door. It is a good idea to check the colour before buying. *1 mark*

Tip: Remember that coloured dyes in fabrics absorb all colours except the colour you can see.

Total 5 Marks

9. **(a)** **Igneous rock** formed from molten material.   *1 mark*

(b) (i) The molten rocks have different sizes of crystals.   *1 mark*
(ii) Hot liquids that cool slowly allow crystals the time to grow large. Rapid cooling gives small crystals.   *2 marks*

(c) Since the lava cools quickly, there will not be time for large crystals to grow. Lava rocks are glassy or contain small crystals.   *1 mark*

Tip: Crystal size tells us about the history of a rock. Large crystals need time to grow; they must cool slowly, underground.

Total 5 Marks

10. **(a)** The unusual result is that copper coins and the copper coloured pin behave differently. One reason might be that the copper coloured pin has a different metal inside, such as iron.   *2 marks*

(b) (i) The magnetism is operating all the time and so the magnetic object sticks permanently.   *1 mark*
(ii) When the switch is closed, a current flows in the coil and this makes a magnetic field. The field only lasts as long as the current flows. Switching off stops it behaving as a magnet.   *2 marks*

Total 5 Marks

11. **(a)** (i) **Copper** is the least reactive; there is no reaction at all.   *1 mark*
(ii) A metal that does not react with acids is unlikely to react with water.   *1 mark*

(b) (i) Vinegar and citric acid both react slowly, with the release of bubbles of gas.   *1 mark*
(ii) Calcium reacts quickly at first with sulphuric acid to give the salt calcium sulphate. Since this is insoluble, it forms a coating round the metal and the reaction slows and stops.   *2 marks*

(c) (i) magnesium + **sulphuric acid** → magnesium sulphate + hydrogen

1 mark

(ii) **Citric acid** is the weakest; it is the slowest with both calcium and magnesium.   *1 mark*

Tip: This is another example of a general reaction:
metal + acid → a salt + hydrogen gas

Total 7 Marks

12. **(a)** You could vary the colour of the light using red and green separately or together and also use daylight. *1 mark*

(b) (i) Examine whether plants grow taller or live/die or look healthy/unhealthy or see how many of the seeds start to grow. *1 mark*
(ii) grow taller – measure with a ruler
live/die – count how many of each
healthy/unhealthy – count how many of each
seeds start to grow – count how many *1 mark*

> Tip: Check that part (b) (i) and (ii) refer to your own choice of factor in part (a).

(c) To make it a fair test you could give one example from:
- constant temperature
- same amount of water
- lights on for equal times
- lights at equal distances
- You may think of other ideas. *1 mark*

Total 4 Marks

13. **(a)** (i) The missing name is **lead nitrate solution**.
Look on the right hand side and see that two new names have appeared, **lead** and **nitrate**. *2 marks*
(ii) Filter the mixture; the lead chloride will be trapped in the filter paper. *1 mark*

> Tip: Check the definitions of all the words about dissolving: solute, solvent, solution, soluble, insoluble.

(b) Use the base **zinc oxide** to prepare the salt zinc sulphate. *1 mark*

(c) $CaCl_2$ is called **calcium chloride**.
$FeSO_4$ is called **iron sulphate**. *2 marks*

The names of salts come from the acids used to prepare them:
Sulphuric acid gives sulphates;
Nitric acid gives nitrates;
Hydrochloric acid gives chlorides.

Total 6 Marks

14. (a) At a temperature of 30°C the first two results are close (36 and 39) but the second repeat is different (62). This suggests that it is wrong.

1 mark

(b) If there is a timing error of 0.5 second as the clock is started or stopped, the effect varies. 0.5s out of 200s is a small error but 0.5s out of 1s is a major error.

2 marks

(c) (i) Draw line graphs, the error will be seen clearly since it will not be near the line.

1 mark

(ii) The conclusion is that the higher the temperature, the less time it takes to change or, the higher the temperature the faster the reaction.

1 mark

Total 5 Marks

15. (a) Electricity → **heat** [1] + **light** [1] or the other way round

2 marks

> *Tip:* Revise energy transfers of different kinds as these often appear in questions.

(b) The low energy lamp turns more of the electricity into light and less into waste heat.

2 marks

(c) Sophie needs to buy and use less electricity since the low energy lamp uses one fifth (20/100) of the power to produce the same amount of light. The less electricity that is used, the less fossil fuel (or other energy source) is required. Pollution should also be less.

2 marks

Total 6 Marks

Total marks on this paper = 81 marks

Achieving the best marks possible

The questions on these practice papers are all linked to the five key scientific ideas taught at Key Stage 3 (years 7–9):
- cells ;
- interdependence ;
- particles ;
- forces ;
- energy.

One important change that began in 2003 is the increased importance of questions about science enquiry and investigative skills. Remember to include this when you prepare for the tests.

The questions are designed to do a range of jobs:
- assess your knowledge and understanding of science;
- assess your recall of facts, processes and skills;
- see how well you can interpret data;
- see if you can explain things using scientific ideas.

Read the clues in the questions. If part of a question has two marks, then you need to write about two things. This may be the answer followed by a reason.

The grade boundary charts show you how well you have performed. When you add up your marks and check the level, there may be some encouraging news. Say you score 101 marks on papers 1 and 2 in the 3–6 tier papers. You may be disappointed that this is level 4. However, if you check the grade boundary, you will see that you would need only 4 more marks to reach level 5. This may mean just half of one extra question being correct next time. Make every mark count.

How to calculate your level

To find out how well you have done in the practice papers:
- add together your marks for paper 1 and paper 2;
- use the table below to find your level;
- make sure you look at the right tier of papers.

Level	Tier 3–6 papers	Tier 5–7 papers
N (means no level achieved)	0–34	0–36
2	35–41	
3	42–72	
4	73–104	37–42
5	105–133	43–73
6	134 or more	74–105
7		106 or more